DESIGNER **KRYSTAL HENNES**

ASSISTANT EDITOR **FREDDYE LINS**

EDITOR **RANDY STRADLEY**

PUBLISHER **MIKE RICHARDSON**

Special thanks to Jann Moorhead, David Anderman, Troy Alders, Leland Chee, Sue Rostoni, and Carol Roeder at Lucas Licensing.

This book collects the short story "Star Wars: The Clone Wars—Opress Unleashed," originally published in *Free Comic Book Day 2011* by Dark Horse Comics.

Published by Dark Horse Books, a division of Dark Horse Comics, Inc.
10956 SE Main Street, Milwaukie, OR 97222

DarkHorse.com | StarWars.com

To find a comics shop in your area, call the Comic Shop Locator Service toll-free at 1.888.266.4226
First edition: November 2011 | ISBN 978-1-59582-766-1

10 9 8 7 6 5 4 3 2 1

PRINTED AT 1010 PRINTING INTERNATIONAL, LTD., GUANGDONG PROVINCE, CHINA

Library of Congress Cataloging-in-Publication Data

Windham, Ryder.
Strange allies / script, Ryder Windham ; art, Ben Dewey ; colors, Mae Hao; lettering, Michael Heisler ; cover art, Stéphane Roux.
p. cm.
At head of title: Star wars. The clone wars.
Summary: "Accompanied by his squad of clone troopers and a hulking swoop biker named Gizz, masterless Jedi Padawan Nuru Kungurama begins a routine protection detail that soon evolves to include a mystery massacre, the hijacking of a space freighter, and the kidnapping of orphaned younglings."--Provided by publisher.
ISBN 978-1-59582-766-1 (alk. paper)
1. Graphic novels. I. Dewey, Ben, 1980- II. Roux, Stéphane. III. Title.
PZ7.7.W56Str 2011
741.5'973--dc23

2011018839

STAR WARS: THE CLONE WARS—STRANGE ALLIES

STRANGE ALLIES

SCRIPT **RYDER WINDHAM** ART **BEN DEWEY**

COLORS **MAE HAO** LETTERING **MICHAEL HEISLER**

COVER ART **STÉPHANE ROUX**

DARK HORSE BOOKS®

THE RISE OF THE EMPIRE
1000–0 YEARS BEFORE *STAR WARS: A NEW HOPE*

The events in these stories take place approximately twenty-two years before the Battle of Yavin.

After the seeming final defeat of the Sith, the Republic enters a state of complacency. In the waning years of the Republic, the Senate is rife with corruption, and the ambitious Senator Palpatine has himself elected Supreme Chancellor. This is the era of the prequel trilogy.

SPACE PIRATES! WE CAN'T OUTRUN THEM!
CAPTAIN! WE'VE JUST LOST TWO THRUSTERS--
--AND OUR PRIMARY SHIELDS ARE DOWN!
THE PIRATES ARE HAILING US, SIR.
PATCH THEM THROUGH. THE FOOLS DON'T KNOW WHO THEY'RE DEALING WITH.

A NEIMOIDIAN?! YOU'RE WITH THE TRADE FEDERATION?
I AM DOOL PUNDAR...
...AND MY TRADE FEDERATION AFFILIATION IS LONG EXPIRED.
SHUT DOWN ALL WEAPONS AND PREPARE TO BE BOARDED BY MY DROIDS. RESIST, AND YOU WILL DIE.
YOU WON'T GET ANY FIGHT FROM US, PUNDAR. BUT BE AWARE THIS FREIGHTER AND ITS CARGO ARE OWNED BY NOGGOX THE HUTT...
...AND NOGGOX WOULD SOONER WORK WITH PIRATES THAN AGAINST THEM.
AND NOGGOX SHOULD BE AWARE...

...I AM A VERY INDEPENDENT OPERATOR.
"PREPARE TO BE BOARDED, CAPTAIN."
BATTLE DROIDS!

THIS FREIGHTER IS NOW MINE, BUT I AM NOT ENTIRELY WITHOUT MERCY.
STUFF THE CAPTAIN AND HIS MEN INTO A LIFEBOAT.
ROGER ROGER.
THIS IS TERRIBLE, CAPTAIN! NOGGOX WILL BE LIVID!
RELAX, LIEUTENANT. WE WEREN'T TRANS-PORTING ANYTHING ILLEGAL, THE FREIGHTER WAS INSURED--
--AND NOGGOX TOLD ME EXACTLY WHAT TO DO IF WE WERE RAIDED BY PIRATES.
TRANSMIT AN EMERGENCY DISTRESS SIGNAL TO CORUSCANT!

"GENERAL YODA, IT HAS COME TO MY ATTENTION THAT THE NEIMOIDIAN PIRATE DOOL PUNDAR HIJACKED A FREIGHTER CARRYING DROID BRAINS--"
--THROUGH AN ASTEROID BELT ALONG SHIPWRIGHTS' TRACE. FORTUNATELY, THE FREIGHTER'S CREW WAS FOUND UNHARMED. BUT THOSE DROID BRAINS WERE CRUCIAL TO THE CONSTRUCTION OF REPUBLIC VESSELS AT FONDOR SHIPYARDS.
SPREAD THIN, OUR FORCES ARE, CHANCELLOR PALPATINE.
DIFFICULT IT WOULD BE, TO SEND JEDI AFTER THE PIRATES.

AS MUCH AS I WANT THE PIRATES BROUGHT TO JUSTICE, MY MORE IMMEDIATE CONCERN IS GETTING THE DROID BRAINS TO FONDOR.
THE STOLEN FREIGHTER BELONGS TO NOGGOX THE HUTT, WHO ALSO OWNS THE DROID-MANUFACTURING FACILITY ON THE PLANET AFFA.
NOGGOX CAN SEND ANOTHER SHIPMENT TO FONDOR, BUT INSISTS UPON A JEDI ESCORT FOR HIS ONE REMAINING FREIGHTER.
INSISTS, HE DOES?
GENERAL YODA, WE NEED THOSE DROID BRAINS FOR OUR FLEET. IS NOT GENERAL FISTO NEAR THE AFFA SYSTEM?
NEAR AFFA, FISTO IS. READILY AVAILABLE, HE IS NOT. NOR AM I. HERE ON CORUSCANT, MY DUTY IS.

PERHAPS... PERHAPS THIS SITUATION DOES NOT REQUIRE A JEDI *GENERAL.*
WHAT ABOUT *NURU KUNGURAMA?* AFTER ALL, DESPITE HIS YOUTH...
"...KUNGURAMA LED *BREAKOUT SQUAD* TO LIBERATE THE PLANET KYNACHI FROM THE TECHNO UNION.

"AND, ALTHOUGH HIS MISSION TO CHISS SPACE HAD SOME SETBACKS...
"...HE HELD HIS OWN AGAINST PIRATES AT A REMOTE BLACK-HOLE SECTOR...

"...AND DISCOVERED AN INFINITY GATE THAT ALLOWED HIM TO RESCUE A TEAM OF XENOARCHAEOLOGISTS.
"ON VACED, HE DEFEATED A MANDALORIAN ASSASSIN...

"... AND HE STOPPED THE TECHNO UNION FROM TRANSFORMING BILBRINGI DEPOT INTO A SECRET MANUFACTURING FACILITY FOR THE CONFEDERACY OF INDEPENDENT SYSTEMS. GENERAL YODA..."

...IS YOUNG KUNGURAMA NOT SUFFICIENTLY QUALIFIED TO DELIVER THE FREIGHTER TO FONDOR?

DEMONSTRATED GREAT INITIATIVE, NURU KUNGURAMA HAS, AND UNDER EXTRAORDINARY CIRCUMSTANCES.

*BUT STILL A **PADAWAN,** HE IS...AND WITHOUT A MASTER.*

FOR THE SAKE OF THE REPUBLIC FLEET, I HOPE YOU WILL RECONSIDER. I CAN ASK NO MORE.
THANK YOU FOR YOUR TIME, GENERAL.

HURMM...

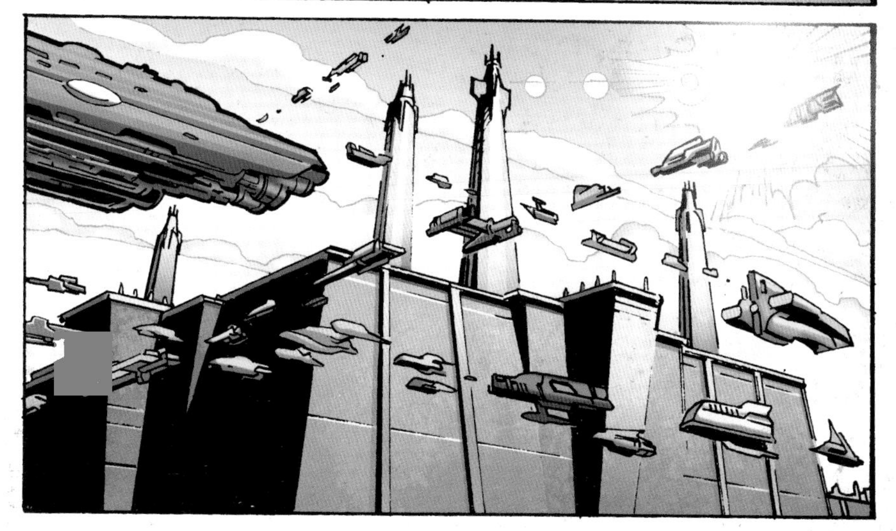

ZANG!

DOW!
BDOW!

ZZZKT!

TELL ME, NURU KUNGURAMA... UNSAFE, IS IT, TO FIGHT TRAINING DROIDS *ALONE?*
WOULD I BE SAFER, MASTER YODA, IF I DEPENDED ON OTHERS TO FIGHT ALONGSIDE ME? AND WITH THE FORCE AS OUR ALLY, CAN A JEDI EVER BE TRULY ALONE?
BUT YOU ARE NOT HERE TO TRADE QUESTIONS. CHANCELLOR PALPATINE HAS ANOTHER SECRET MISSION FOR BREAKOUT SQUAD AND ME.
HEARD THIS FROM THE CHANCELLOR'S OFFICE, DID YOU?
NO, MASTER. WHEN I SAW YOU IN THE DOORWAY, I JUST...*KNEW.*
CORRECT, YOU ARE, YOUNG NURU. YOUR HELP, ONCE AGAIN, THE REPUBLIC NEEDS.
BRIEF YOU, I SHALL, BEFORE YOU ASSEMBLE YOUR TEAM...

GREETINGS, NURU! ALWAYS GOOD TO SEE YOU! WHATEVER YOU'RE HUNGRY FOR...
...IT'S MY TREAT!
THANK YOU, DEXTER, BUT I REGRET I'M IN A HURRY. I'M ONLY HERE TO GET--
GIZZ! PUT ME DOWN, YOU BIG LOUT!

WHAT'S WRONG, HERMIONE? DON'T TELL ME YOU NEVER GOT PICKED UP BEFORE.
YOU'LL BE PICKING A FORK OUT OF YOUR UGLY HEAD IF YOU DON'T PUT ME DOWN NOW!
GIZZ! LET HER GO.
I WAS JUST JOKIN', DOLL. YOU SAID YOU LIKE FUNNY GUYS.
I SAID I LIKE GUYS WITH A SENSE OF HUMOR! I ALSO SAID I LIKE SMART GUYS!
THE WAY YOU COME IN EVERY DAY, LOOKING AT THE MENU FOR HOURS...I BET YOU DON'T EVEN KNOW HOW TO READ!
THAT'S NOT...
I WASN'T JUST LOOKING AT THE MENU.

GIZZ! HEY, GIZZ! WAIT UP!
ARE YOU ALL RIGHT? WHAT EXACTLY HAPPENED BACK--?
WOMEN.
I BEG YOUR PARDON?
YOU WOULDN'T UNDERSTAND, KID--YOU'RE A JEDI.
AW, JUST FORGET IT ALREADY. *I* HAVE.
SAY, HOW COME YOU'RE FOLLOWING ME?
I'VE BEEN GIVEN AN ASSIGNMENT WITH BREAKOUT SQUAD. I DON'T KNOW WHETHER YOUR *SPECIAL TALENTS* MIGHT BE REQUIRED, BUT I WOULD BE MOST GRATEFUL IF YOU ACCOMPANIED US.

YOU WANT *ME?* I'M JUST A SWOOP BIKER WHO CAN KNOCK THINGS DOWN. BEYOND THAT, I'M NO GOOD.
HECK, EVEN YOUR HANDLERS SAID YOU SHOULD'VE LEFT ME TO THE AUTHORITIES ON *VACED!*
AND I TOLD THE JEDI COUNCIL I MIGHT NOT HAVE SURVIVED THE VACED MISSION WITHOUT YOUR HELP. IF THEY HAVE ANY OBJECTION TO MY DECISIONS, THEY CAN LECTURE ME LATER.
I BELIEVE YOU'RE A GREAT ALLY, GIZZ. WHAT DO YOU SAY? ARE YOU WITH ME?
HMM. THIS NEW ASSIGNMENT YOU MENTIONED... WOULD I GET TO HIT ANYONE?
WELL, I *DO* STRIVE TO AVOID FIGHTS, BUT IF WE ENCOUNTER PIRATES WHO REFUSE TO SURRENDER --
PIRATES?! OH, HAPPY DAY!
I TAKE IT YOU'RE WITH ME?
I'M A FREE AGENT! NOBODY PULLS MY STRINGS!
LET'S GO!

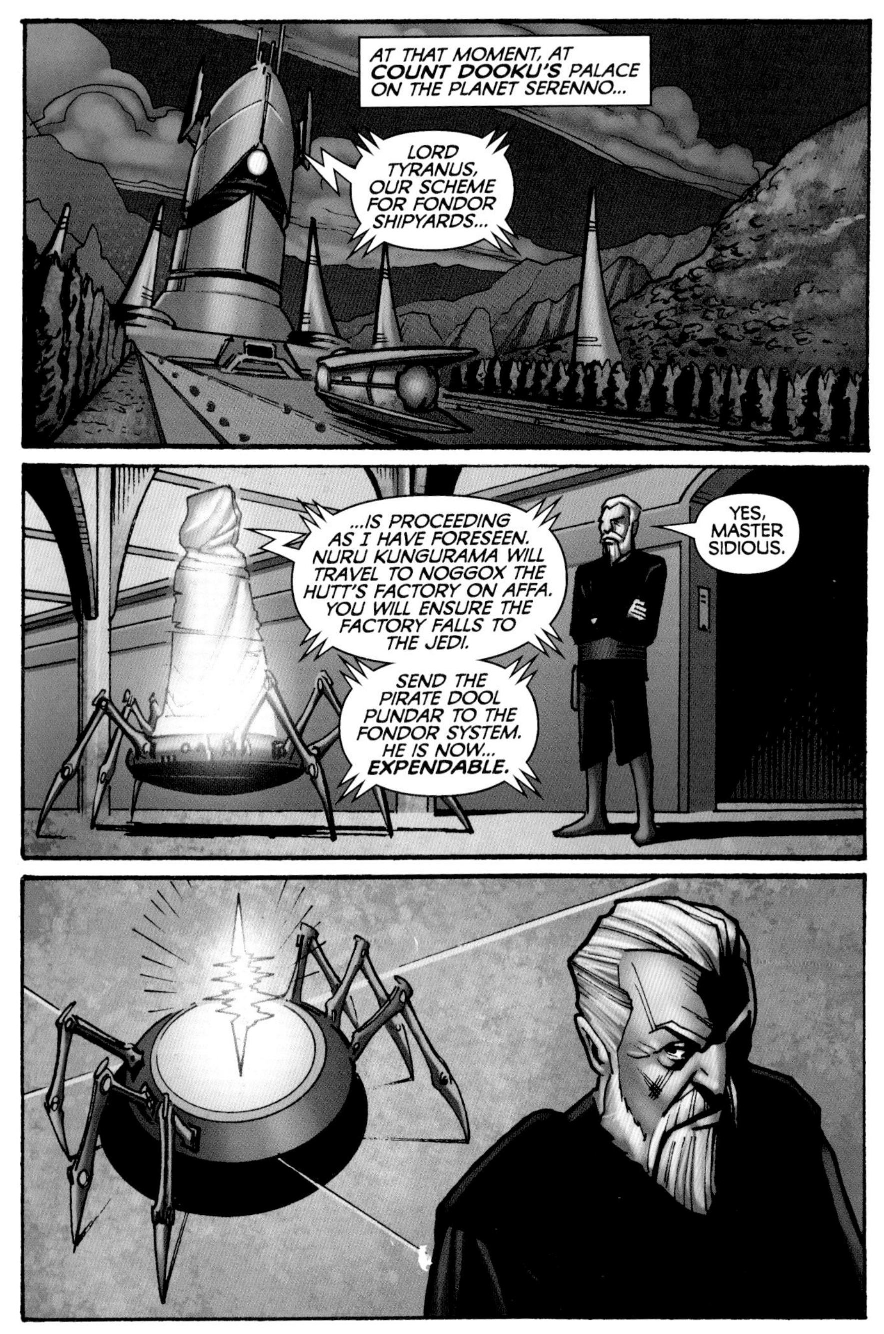
AT THAT MOMENT, AT COUNT DOOKU'S PALACE ON THE PLANET SERENNO...
LORD TYRANUS, OUR SCHEME FOR FONDOR SHIPYARDS...
...IS PROCEEDING AS I HAVE FORESEEN. NURU KUNGURAMA WILL TRAVEL TO NOGGOX THE HUTT'S FACTORY ON AFFA. YOU WILL ENSURE THE FACTORY FALLS TO THE JEDI.
SEND THE PIRATE DOOL PUNDAR TO THE FONDOR SYSTEM. HE IS NOW... EXPENDABLE.
YES, MASTER SIDIOUS.

SAVAGE OPRESS. I HAVE A MISSION FOR YOU ON AFFA. YOUR INSTRUCTIONS ARE ON THIS DATADISC.
I KILL FOR YOU... AGAIN.
YES, OF COURSE, YOU SHALL KILL.
YOU MAY TAKE MY SHIP. BRING IT BACK IN ONE PIECE.
YES, MASTER.

ATTENTION! JEDI COMMANDER ON DECK!
AT EASE, MEN.
KNUCKLES... BREAKER...SHARP... CHATTERBOX...IT'S GOOD TO SEE YOU ALL. YOU REMEMBER GIZZ.
GOOD TO HAVE YOU BOTH BACK WITH US, COMMANDER.
HEY, BREAKER-- WHERE'S CLEAVER?
ALREADY ON BOARD THE SHUTTLE, MASTER GIZZMAN. HE'S MEDITATING.
JUST CALL ME "GIZZ."
THE DROID... MEDITATES?
WELL, HE DOES WANT TO BECOME A JEDI.

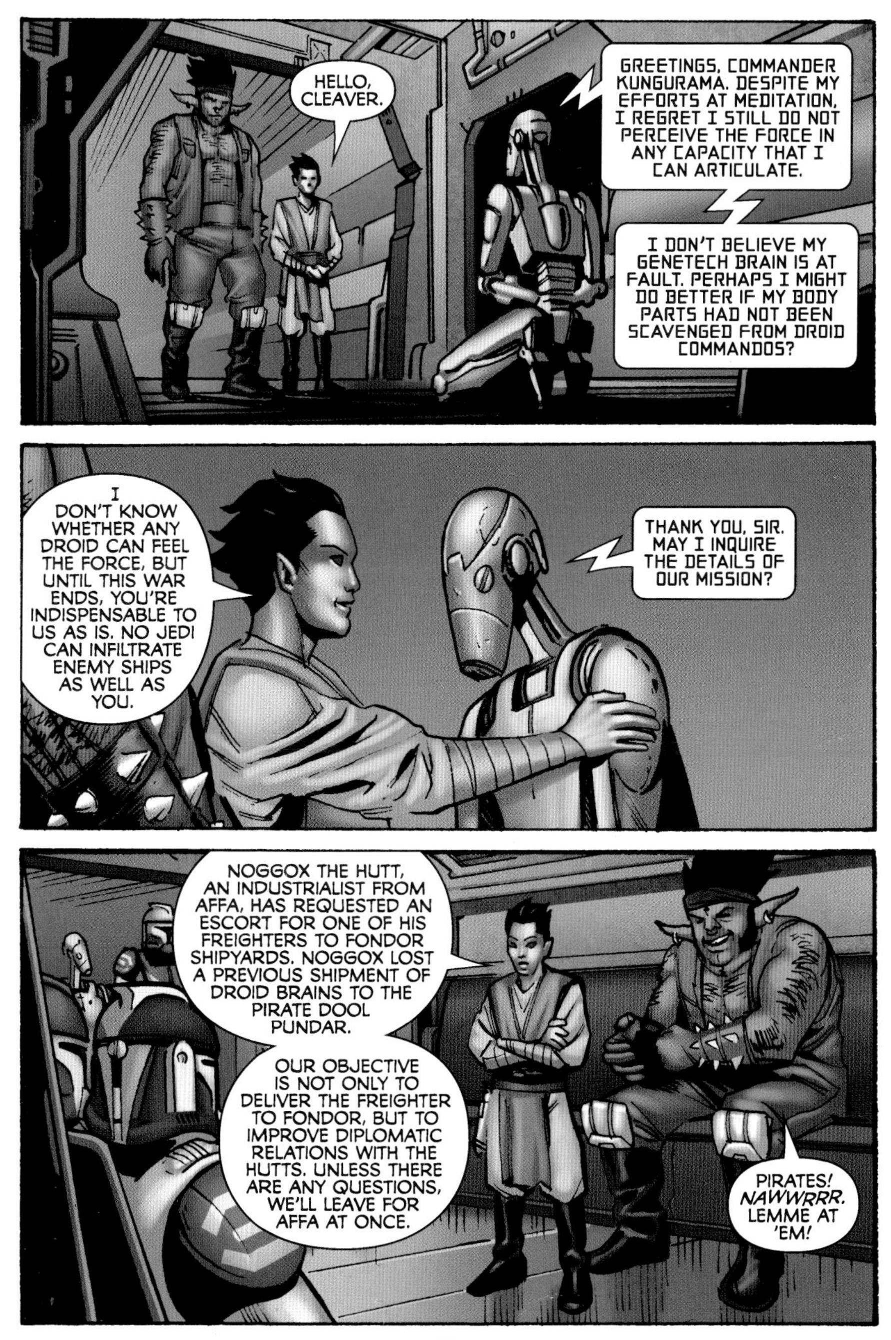
HELLO, CLEAVER.
GREETINGS, COMMANDER KUNGURAMA. DESPITE MY EFFORTS AT MEDITATION, I REGRET I STILL DO NOT PERCEIVE THE FORCE IN ANY CAPACITY THAT I CAN ARTICULATE.
I DON'T BELIEVE MY GENETECH BRAIN IS AT FAULT. PERHAPS I MIGHT DO BETTER IF MY BODY PARTS HAD NOT BEEN SCAVENGED FROM DROID COMMANDOS?
I DON'T KNOW WHETHER ANY DROID CAN FEEL THE FORCE, BUT UNTIL THIS WAR ENDS, YOU'RE INDISPENSABLE TO US AS IS. NO JEDI CAN INFILTRATE ENEMY SHIPS AS WELL AS YOU.
THANK YOU, SIR. MAY I INQUIRE THE DETAILS OF OUR MISSION?
NOGGOX THE HUTT, AN INDUSTRIALIST FROM AFFA, HAS REQUESTED AN ESCORT FOR ONE OF HIS FREIGHTERS TO FONDOR SHIPYARDS. NOGGOX LOST A PREVIOUS SHIPMENT OF DROID BRAINS TO THE PIRATE DOOL PUNDAR.
OUR OBJECTIVE IS NOT ONLY TO DELIVER THE FREIGHTER TO FONDOR, BUT TO IMPROVE DIPLOMATIC RELATIONS WITH THE HUTTS. UNLESS THERE ARE ANY QUESTIONS, WE'LL LEAVE FOR AFFA AT ONCE.
PIRATES! *NAWWRRR.* LEMME AT 'EM!

PERMISSION TO SPEAK *PRIVATELY,* COMMANDER?
GO AHEAD, BREAKER.
GIZZ IS A GOOD FIGHTER, BUT... HE'S A LOOSE CANNON. MAY I ASK WHY YOU BROUGHT HIM?
BECAUSE A LOOSE CANNON IS NOT A LOST CAUSE, AND HE CAN BENEFIT FROM AN ENCOURAGING NUDGE.
ALSO, WE'RE DEALING WITH A HUTT AND MAYBE PIRATES TOO. IF ANYTHING UNEXPECTED HAPPENS BETWEEN AFFA AND FONDOR...
...WE MIGHT *NEED* THAT EXTRA CANNON.

O, MIGHTY NOGGOX! WE CAUGHT THIS GUY SKULKING AROUND BEHIND THE MAIN HANGAR...
...AND HE WAS CARRYING THIS WEAPON. HE DIDN'T PUT UP A FIGHT.
NICE AXE.
WHAT BRINGS YOU TO THE PLANET AFFA, STRANGER?
YOU ARE IN DANGER. A JEDI APPROACHES...

BWAH-HAW-HAW!
OH, MY, THAT IS A GUT BUSTER.
I APPRECIATE THE WARNING, FRIEND. BUT AS YOU CAN SEE, I'M IN LITTLE DANGER.
MY FORTRESS'S DEFENSES ARE STATE OF THE ART. MY GUARDS ARE AS LOYAL AS THEY ARE DEADLY. YOU WERE WISE TO SURRENDER.
AS FOR THE JEDI, IT MAY SURPRISE YOU TO KNOW I'M EXPECTING HIS ARRIVAL WITHIN THE HOUR. AFTER ALL...
...I INVITED HIM!

TWO OF MY FREIGHTERS, CARRYING PARTS FOR REPUBLIC VESSELS TO FONDOR SHIPYARDS, WERE RECENTLY RAIDED BY SPACE PIRATES.
THE JEDI CLAIMS THESE PIRATES ARE IN LEAGUE WITH THE CONFEDERACY OF INDEPENDENT SYSTEMS.
HE HAS OFFERED TO ESCORT MY OTHER FREIGHTERS TO FONDOR.
PERSONALLY, I HOPE THE JEDI, THE PIRATES, AND THE CONFEDERACY SLAUGHTER EACH OTHER!
I'M CURIOUS... HOW DID YOU LEARN OF THE JEDI TRAVELING TO AFFA?
COUNT DOOKU.
DOOKU?
YOU ARE IN DANGER... BECAUSE DOOKU KNOWS YOU INVITED THE JEDI.

WHAT TH--?!
STOP HIM!
GAH!
NUH! AKKTH--!
WHUK
WHUK

STOP! I HAVE MONEY! I CAN--!
WHUK
WHUK
WHUK
WHUK

YOU COMPLETED THE ASSIGNMENT?
YES, MASTER.
WELL DONE, **SAVAGE OPRESS.** RETURN TO ME AT ONCE.
BUT...THE JEDI HAS NOT YET ARRIVED. I COULD--
YOU WILL LEAVE AFFA **NOW.**
YES, MASTER.

WE'RE APPROACHING NOGGOX'S FACTORY, COMMANDER KUNGURAMA...
...BUT THERE'S NO RESPONSE FROM HIS LANDING CONTROLLER.
NOGGOX IS EXPECTING US, BREAKER.
TELL CHATTERBOX TO LAND AT THE COORDINATES NOGGOX PROVIDED EARLIER.
DID CHANCELLOR PALPATINE REALLY BELIEVE THE HUTT *WANTS* OUR HELP, COMMANDER?
I DOUBT THE CHANCELLOR WOULD HAVE ENCOURAGED THIS MISSION OTHERWISE, KNUCKLES. BUT IF SOMETHING *HAS* GONE WRONG...
...WE'RE FORTUNATE TO HAVE *CLEAVER* AND *GIZZ* ON OUR SIDE!
THANK YOU, COMMANDER.
HUMPH! HERE'S HOPING I GET TO HIT *SOMETHING* SOON!

STRANGE THAT NO ONE IS HERE TO GREET US. PERHAPS YOU SHOULD WAIT HERE, COMMANDER.
NO, BREAKER. WE'RE ALL STICKING TOGETHER.
COME ON. LET'S TAKE A LOOK INSIDE.
WHAT'S THAT ODOR?
RAW MEAT! WE MUST BE CLOSE TO A KITCHEN.
QUIET, GIZZ! THERE'S A LIGHT UP...
...AHEAD.
WELL, I WAS *RIGHT* ABOUT THE RAW MEAT!
DOES THIS MEAN OUR MISSION IS OVER?
NO, CLEAVER. NOT UNTIL WE FIND OUT WHAT HAPPENED HERE!

MOST DISTURBING, YOUR REPORT IS, NURU. NOGGOX AND HIS GUARDS WERE KILLED HOW?
POSSIBLY BY A GANG USING VIBRO-AXES. SOME OF NOGGOX'S GUARDS NEVER DREW THEIR OWN WEAPONS. THE ATTACK WAS PROBABLY AS SWIFT AS IT WAS VICIOUS.
WE'VE SECURED NOGGOX'S FACTORY. IT APPEARS HIS FREIGHTER WAS UNTOUCHED. HOW SHALL WE PROCEED?
HURMM... INDEPENDENT, NOGGOX WAS, OF THE HUTT GRAND COUNCIL. CRUCIAL TO OUR FLEET, THAT FREIGHTER'S CARGO IS. BEHIND THE KILLINGS, THE SEPARATISTS MAY BE.
TO FONDOR SHIPYARDS, YOU WILL BRING THE DROID BRAINS. BUT BECAUSE SOMETHING MURKY ABOUT THIS MISSION I SENSED...
...ASSISTANCE YOU WILL HAVE.
ASSISTANCE?
AVAILABLE, ANOTHER JEDI BECAME. IMMINENT, HIS ARRIVAL ON AFFA IS.
MAY THE FORCE BE WITH YOU, NURU.
COMMANDER! A JEDI STARFIGHTER IS APPROACHING!

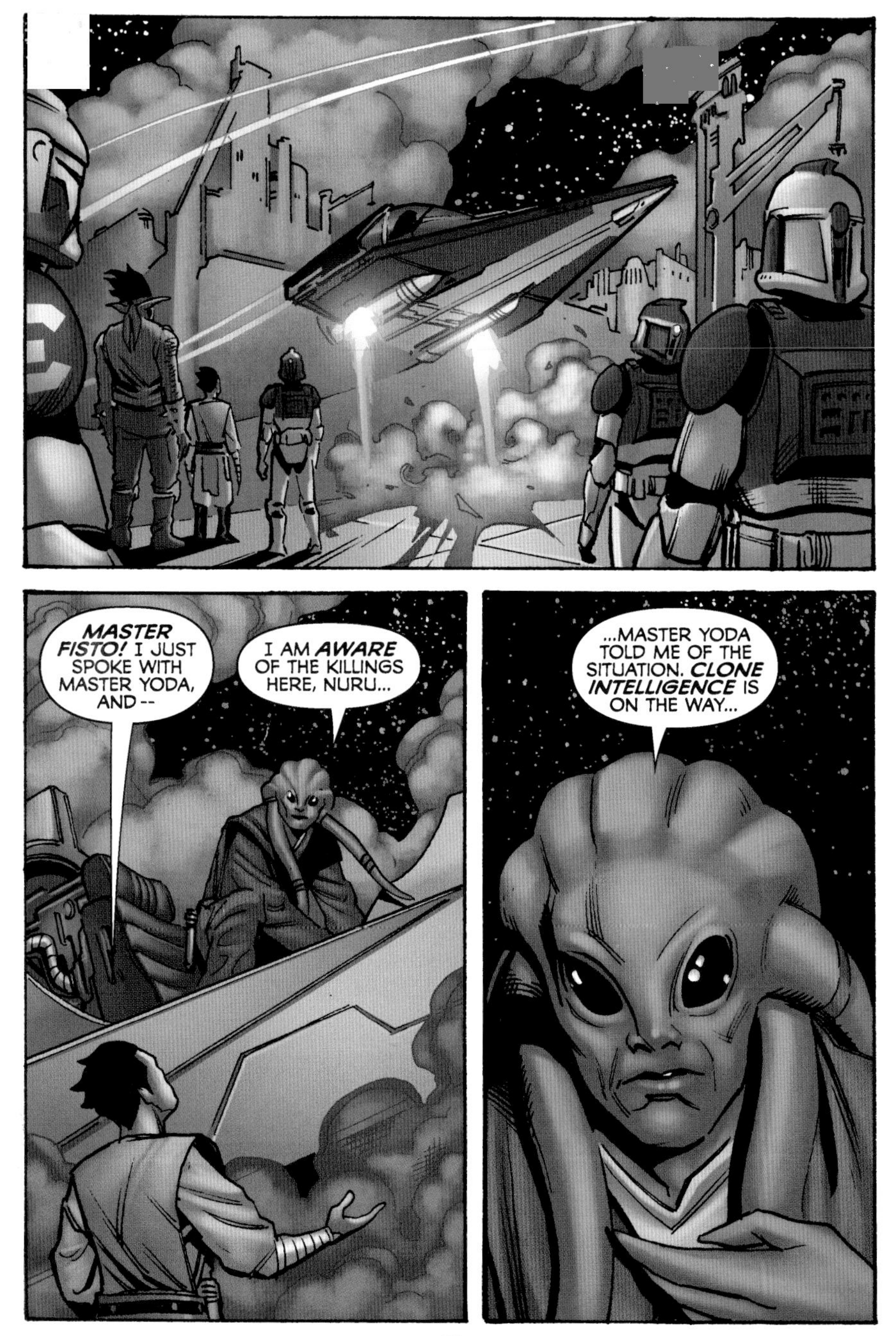
MASTER FISTO! I JUST SPOKE WITH MASTER YODA, AND --
I AM AWARE OF THE KILLINGS HERE, NURU...
...MASTER YODA TOLD ME OF THE SITUATION. CLONE INTELLIGENCE IS ON THE WAY...

...LEAVE THE CRIME SCENE FOR THEM. OUR PRIORITY IS TO GET TO FONDOR.
WE'LL PLACE MY FIGHTER IN THE FREIGHTER'S DOCKING BAY. NURU, YOU AND I WILL TAKE THE FREIGHTER WHILE THE OTHERS --
WHOA!
WHO'S GIVING THE ORDERS?
MASTER FISTO IS A JEDI GENERAL, GIZZ. HE OUTRANKS ME.
BUT...GIZZ IS CORRECT, NURU. THIS IS YOUR ASSIGNMENT.
OUR ORDERS, COMMANDER?
I...WE'LL TAKE THE FREIGHTER. GIZZ COMES WITH US.
GOOD THINKING, PAL. LET'S GO!

MASTER FISTO, I APOLOGIZE FOR GIZZ'S BEHAVIOR. I'LL EXPLAIN TO HIM THAT YOU'RE THE COMMANDING OFFICER...
ZZZ...
...AS SOON AS HE WAKES UP.
YOUR APOLOGY IS UNNECESSARY, NURU. LIKE THE OTHER MEMBERS OF THE JEDI COUNCIL, I'VE REVIEWED THE REPORTS OF YOUR *PREVIOUS MISSIONS* WITH GIZZ.
YOU TWO HAVE GAINED QUITE A REPUTATION. WHILE OTHERS QUESTION YOUR REASONING TO ALLY WITH AN OUTLAW, I DO NOT. MORE THAN ONCE, HE HELPED KEEP YOU ALIVE.
EVERY JEDI SHOULD HAVE SUCH FRIENDS, ESPECIALLY DURING THIS AWFUL WAR.
AH. THE FONDOR SYSTEM IS JUST AHEAD!

FISTO TO BREAKOUT SQUAD. PREPARE TO EXIT HYPERSPACE.
WE'RE ALL SET, GENERAL.
MASTER FISTO, I...I REGRET I NEVER TOLD YOU HOW SADDENED I WAS BY THE LOSS OF YOUR FORMER PADAWAN, NAHDAR VEBB.
AND I SHOULD HAVE GIVEN YOU MY CONDOLENCES FOR LANCHU SKAA. I WAS WITH YOUR LATE MASTER WHEN HE WAS FELLED ON GEONOSIS.
AS FOR YOUR SECOND MASTER, RING-SOL AMBASE...
...I HOPE HE IS AT PEACE.
YOU'D BETTER WAKE GIZZ AND TELL HIM TO FASTEN HIS SAFETY HARNESS. WE'RE COMING UP ON THE EXIT NOW...

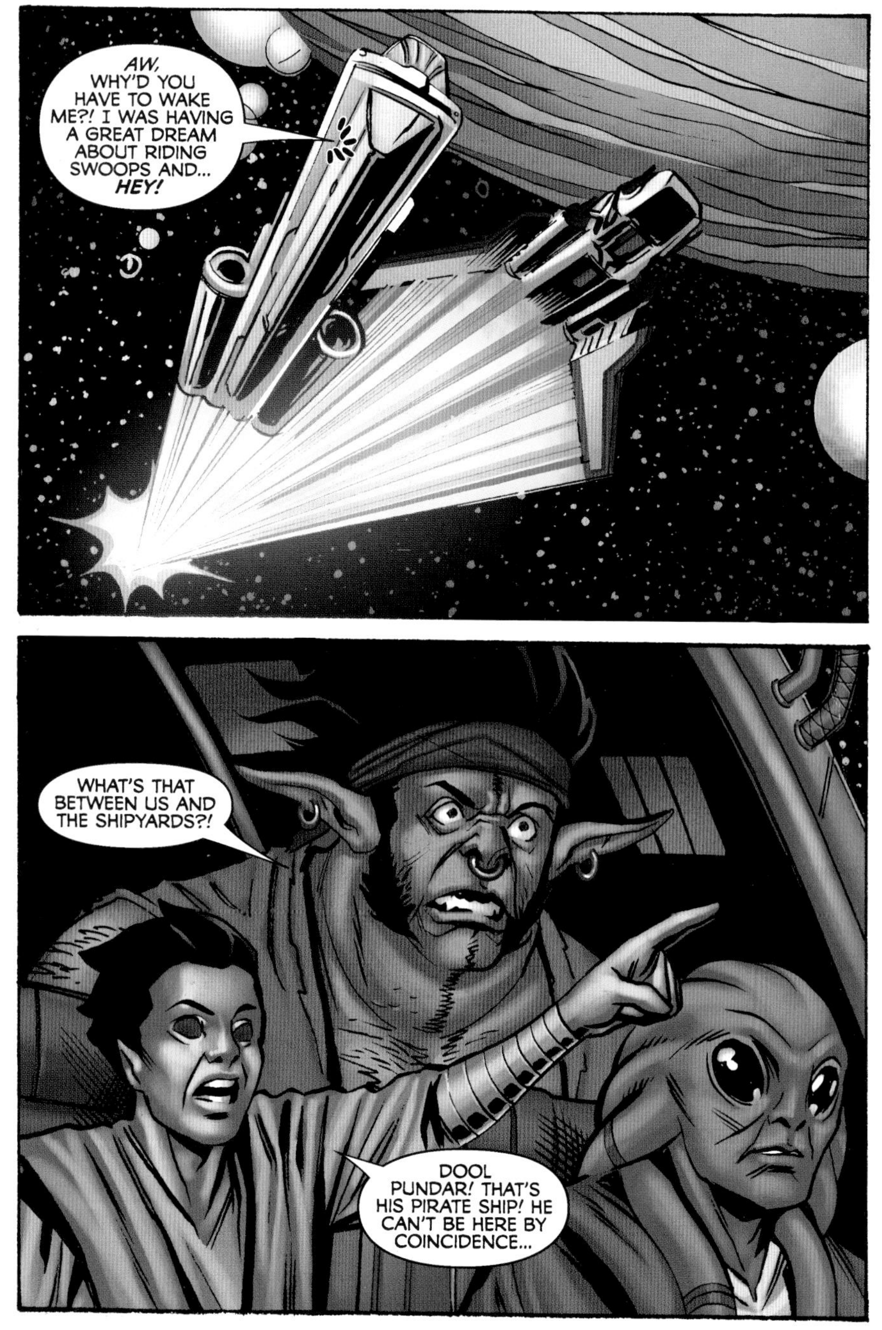

AW, WHY'D YOU HAVE TO WAKE ME?! I WAS HAVING A GREAT DREAM ABOUT RIDING SWOOPS AND... HEY!
WHAT'S THAT BETWEEN US AND THE SHIPYARDS?!
DOOL PUNDAR! THAT'S HIS PIRATE SHIP! HE CAN'T BE HERE BY COINCIDENCE...

LET'S PONDER THAT LATER, NURU. TWELVE VULTURE DROIDS APPROACHING FAST...
...AND THIS FREIGHTER CAN'T OUTRUN THEM.
STICK CLOSE WITH THE ATTACK SHUTTLE WHILE I GO TO MY STARFIGHTER.
GIZZ. TAKE THE LASER CANNON.
YEAH!

THEY'RE FIRING AT US!
THIS IS GENERAL KIT FISTO OF THE ARMY OF THE REPUBLIC...
...DOOL PUNDAR, YOU WILL SURRENDER AT ONCE.
A JEDI AND AN ATTACK SHUTTLE?! BUT...COUNT DOOKU SAID NOGGOX'S FREIGHTER WOULD BE UNPROTECTED!
BAH! DIRECT ALL FIREPOWER AT THE FREIGHTER! THAT SHOULD KEEP THE JEDI AND HIS PET CLONES BUSY!

AW, POODOO! THEY'RE SWARMING US, KID!
THEN LET'S LEAD THE SWARM STRAIGHT BACK TO THEIR HIVE. BRACE YOURSELF!
THIS IS GONNA HURT.

C'MON, NURU! LET'S FIND DOOL PUNDAR AND GET THIS DONE!
CAPTAIN! WE'VE BEEN BOARDED BY A JEDI!
THIS IS DOOKU'S FAULT! TO THE ESCAPE PODS!
NURU, DO YOU READ ME? THE PIRATES ARE ABANDONING SHIP! NURU?

COPY, MASTER. THE FREIGHTER TOOK A HAMMERING, BUT IT WILL STILL FLY. WE CAN PURSUE DOOL PUNDAR AND HIS--
WE CAN'T ALLOW THE PIRATES TO DISTRACT US FROM OUR OBJECTIVE, NURU. WE MUST GET THE DROID BRAINS TO FONDOR.
I'LL ALERT FONDOR SPACE PATROL TO IMPOUND PUNDAR'S BATTLESHIP AND COLLECT THE ESCAPE PODS WHILE YOU BRING OUT THE FREIGHTER.
WHAT'S WITH FISTO? HE'D RATHER BE A DELIVERY BOY THAN FIGHT?
A JEDI NEVER PREFERS TO FIGHT, GIZZ, BUT FIGHTS ONLY WHEN NECESSARY.
WELL...IF YOU ASK ME, WHEN YOU'VE GOT SOMEONE ON THE RUN, IT'S USUALLY BEST YOU DON'T LET THEM RUN AWAY.

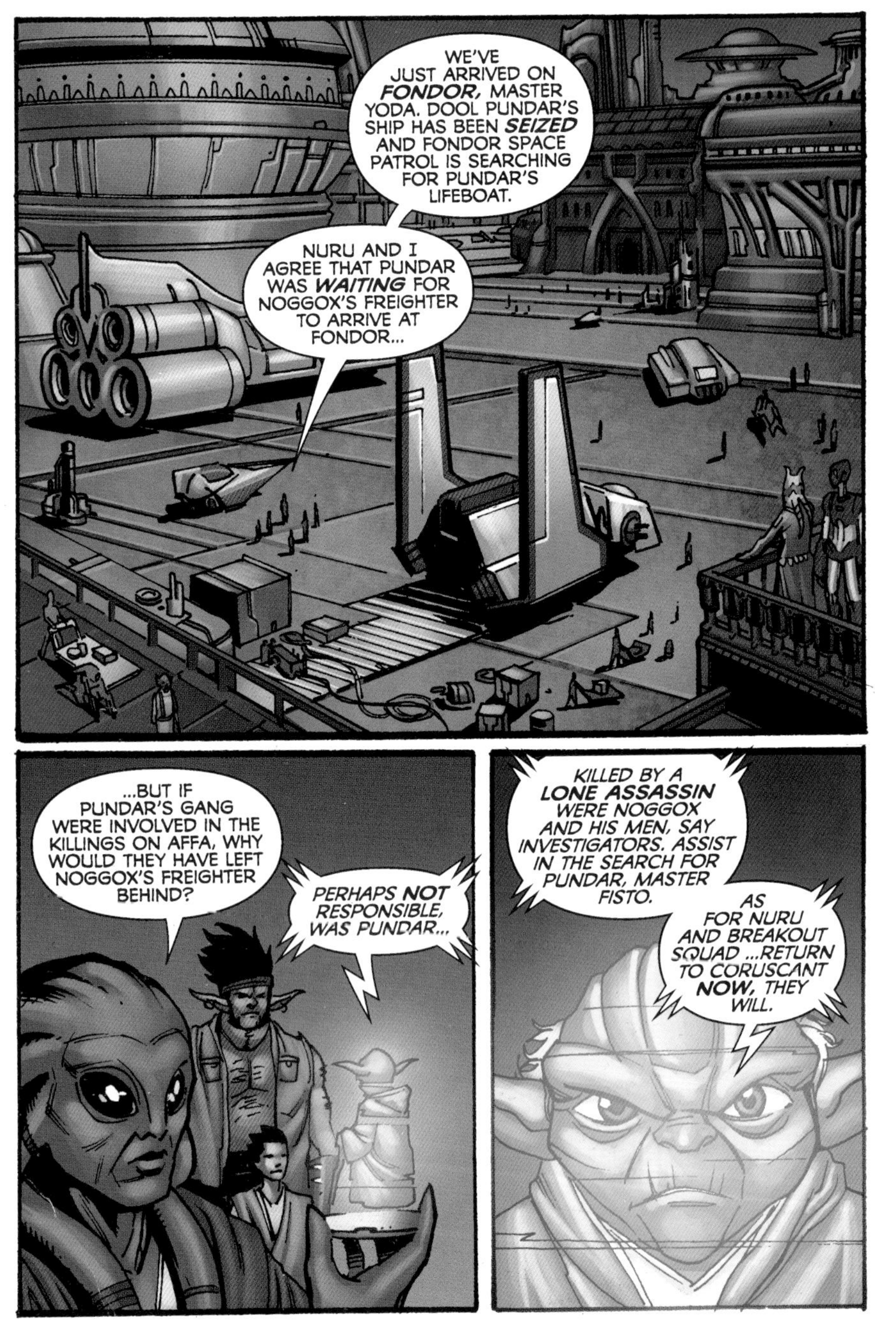
WE'VE JUST ARRIVED ON FONDOR, MASTER YODA. DOOL PUNDAR'S SHIP HAS BEEN SEIZED AND FONDOR SPACE PATROL IS SEARCHING FOR PUNDAR'S LIFEBOAT.
NURU AND I AGREE THAT PUNDAR WAS WAITING FOR NOGGOX'S FREIGHTER TO ARRIVE AT FONDOR...
...BUT IF PUNDAR'S GANG WERE INVOLVED IN THE KILLINGS ON AFFA, WHY WOULD THEY HAVE LEFT NOGGOX'S FREIGHTER BEHIND?
PERHAPS NOT RESPONSIBLE, WAS PUNDAR...
KILLED BY A LONE ASSASSIN WERE NOGGOX AND HIS MEN, SAY INVESTIGATORS. ASSIST IN THE SEARCH FOR PUNDAR, MASTER FISTO.
AS FOR NURU AND BREAKOUT SQUAD ...RETURN TO CORUSCANT NOW, THEY WILL.

SOME JEDI HAVE ALL THE LUCK! FISTO GETS TO HUNT PIRATES WHILE WE GOTTA GO BACK TO CORUSCANT? THAT REALLY *GNAWS!*
EXCUSE ME? HELLO?
I OVER-HEARD YOU SPEAK OF JEDI AND CORUSCANT. ARE YOU A JEDI?
ME? I... *UH,* I DON'T... THAT IS...
I AM NURU KUNGURAMA, A JEDI. MY LOQUACIOUS FRIEND HERE IS GIZZ. MAY WE BE OF SERVICE?

I AM KUVUTA PINDI, A VOLUNTEER FOR REPUBLIC CHILDREN'S AID. I WAS ESCORTING THESE ORPHANED CHILDREN TO A PLACEMENT CENTER ON THE PLANET FOLESS, BUT...
...THE TRANSPORT I'D HIRED TO MEET US HERE YESTERDAY NEVER ARRIVED. I... I'M AFRAID I WAS SWINDLED!
I'M SORRY TO BOTHER YOU WITH MY TROUBLES, BUT I DON'T KNOW WHERE ELSE TO TURN, AND THE CHILDREN...
...THEY'VE ALREADY LOST SO MUCH.
YOU...DON'T YOU WORRY YOUR PRETTY...I MEAN... COUNT ON US TO GET YOU AND THE KIDS TO FOLESS!
BUT...GIZZ, MASTER YODA ORDERED US TO RETURN--
WHEN WE TELL HIM WE WERE HELPING ORPHANS, HE'LL UNDERSTAND.
CHOMP!

OUCH!
DON'T DO THAT AGAIN.
PROBLEM HERE, COMMANDER?
A POSSIBLE CHANGE IN PLANS, BREAKER.
HOW LONG WOULD OUR RETURN TO CORUSCANT BE DELAYED IF WE STOPPED AT FOLESS?
MAYBE AN HOUR OR SO...
VERY WELL. INFORM THE OTHERS WE'LL BE TAKING THESE CIVILIANS TO FOLESS.
UH-OH. GIZZ IS SMITTEN.
AGAIN.

SO... UH, MISTRESS PINDI? WOULD YOU MIND IF I SAT NEXT TO YOU?
NOT AT ALL, GIZZ. BUT PLEASE, CALL ME KUVUTA.
IF YOU DON'T MIND MY SAYING SO, KUVUTA...
YOU READ ME, MISTER?
WHAT'D YOU SAY, SHORTY?
READ ME STORY. A GOOD ONE. OKAY?
HEH. CUTE KID.
SO... KUVUTA, I WAS ABOUT TO SAY... YOU GOT REALLY NICE EYES.

WHY... WHY WOULD YOU SAY THAT? ARE YOU... JOKING?
HECK NO! I NEVER SEEN A TWI'LEK WITH EYES LIKE YOURS.
MISTRESS PINDI IS BLIND.
BLIND?
YOU CAN'T READ. YOU STUPID.
WHAT?! I CAN READ, YOU LITTLE...!
PLEASE DON'T BE ANGRY WITH LITTLE CHARKY. AND FORGIVE ME, GIZZ... FOR THINKING YOU WERE JOKING.
YOU... YOU REALLY COULDN'T TELL I WAS BLIND?
I HAD NO IDEA.
YOU UGLY, TOO.

BUT I DON'T LIKE BEING IN HYPERSPACE!
HOW MANY PARSECS TO FOLESS?
WURNDELL THREW UP... AGAIN.
YOU'RE SITTING ON MY LEKKU!
I GOTTA GO TO THE 'FRESHER NOW!
GIZZ! TRAVELING WITH THIS GROUP WAS YOUR IDEA. COULD YOU PLEASE HELP GET THEM CALMED DOWN?
IN A MINUTE, KID. I'M KINDA BUSY.
YOU'RE VERY SWEET, GIZZ. I SUSPECT YOU'VE BROKEN A LOT OF HEARTS.
ME? UH...
HAW! MISTRESS PINDI FUNNY!

GIZZ!
TAKE IT EASY, PAL. THE KIDS ARE JUST HAVING FUN AND --
MISTRESS PINDI STUPID AND UGLY, TOO.
OH...THAT TEARS IT.
GIZZ? CHARKY? WHERE --?
LEGGO ME! PUMMEE DOWN!

GOOD RIDDANCE, YA DISRESPECTFUL PUNK!
WHAT DO YOU THINK YOU'RE --
I GOT THIS UNDER CONTROL, NURU.
ANYONE ELSE WANTS TO BE RUDE OR ACT UP, YOU CAN FOLLOW YOUR FRIEND CHARKY STRAIGHT OUT THE AIRLOCK!
BWAAAGH!

CHILDREN! WHAT HAPPENED? WHERE IS --
WAAAGH! THE BIG MAN THREW CHARKY OUT OF THE SHIP!
G-G-GIZZ... K-KILLED CHARKY! WAWW!
GIZZ...?! OH, NO! WHERE'S THE JEDI? HELP! HELP!
I'M RIGHT HERE, MISTRESS PINDI.
ARE YOU READY TO TELL THEM, GIZZ, OR SHALL I?
ER...I...
I WAS JUST MESSING WITH THE KIDS. TO MAKE THEM BEHAVE.
IT'S NOT AN AIRLOCK. IT'S A UTILITY CLOSET.
COZY IN HERE. YOU SO, SO STUPID.

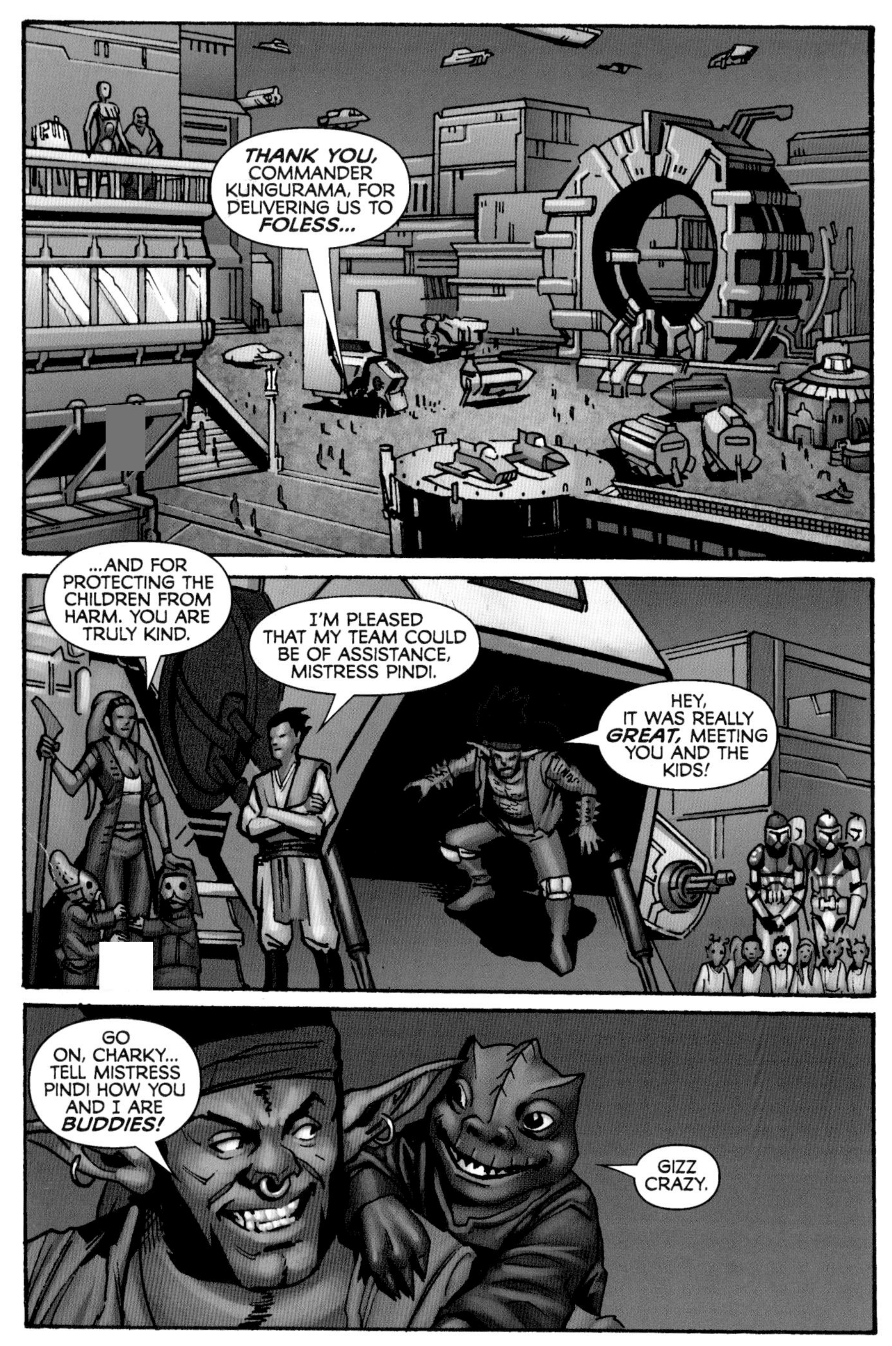
THANK YOU, COMMANDER KUNGURAMA, FOR DELIVERING US TO FOLESS...
...AND FOR PROTECTING THE CHILDREN FROM HARM. YOU ARE TRULY KIND.
I'M PLEASED THAT MY TEAM COULD BE OF ASSISTANCE, MISTRESS PINDI.
HEY, IT WAS REALLY GREAT, MEETING YOU AND THE KIDS!
GO ON, CHARKY... TELL MISTRESS PINDI HOW YOU AND I ARE BUDDIES!
GIZZ CRAZY.

KUVUTA, I...I'M SORRY ABOUT THE PRANK I PULLED. I HOPE WE'LL SEE EACH OTHER...*UH,* I MEAN, ***MEET*** AGAIN.
I JUST WANT YOU TO KNOW I...I THINK YOU'RE --
COME ALONG, CHILDREN. WE'LL TAKE THE GREEN AIR BUS TO THE ***PLACEMENT CENTER.***
I DON'T GET IT. I JUST DON'T GET IT.
IT WAS OBVIOUS YOU WERE QUITE FOND OF MISTRESS PINDI, BUT...
OH, I'M NOT TALKING ABOUT ***FEELINGS,*** KID...
YOU, THERE!

FOLESS SPACEPORT AUTHORITY. YOU ARE...?
I'M NURU KUNGURAMA, A JEDI.
YOU ARRIVED WITH A FEMALE TWI'LEK--
--WHO MATCHES THE DESCRIPTION OF A WOMAN WHO ABDUCTED TEN ORPHANS FROM ABREGADO-RAE, AND TOOK THEM TO FONDOR.
TELL ME...DOES REPUBLIC CHILDREN'S AID HAVE A PLACEMENT CENTER FOR ORPHANS ON FOLESS?
NO. WHY?
THE AIR BUS THAT JUST LEFT...WE HAVE TO STOP IT!
WHERE'S GIZZ?
VROOOM!

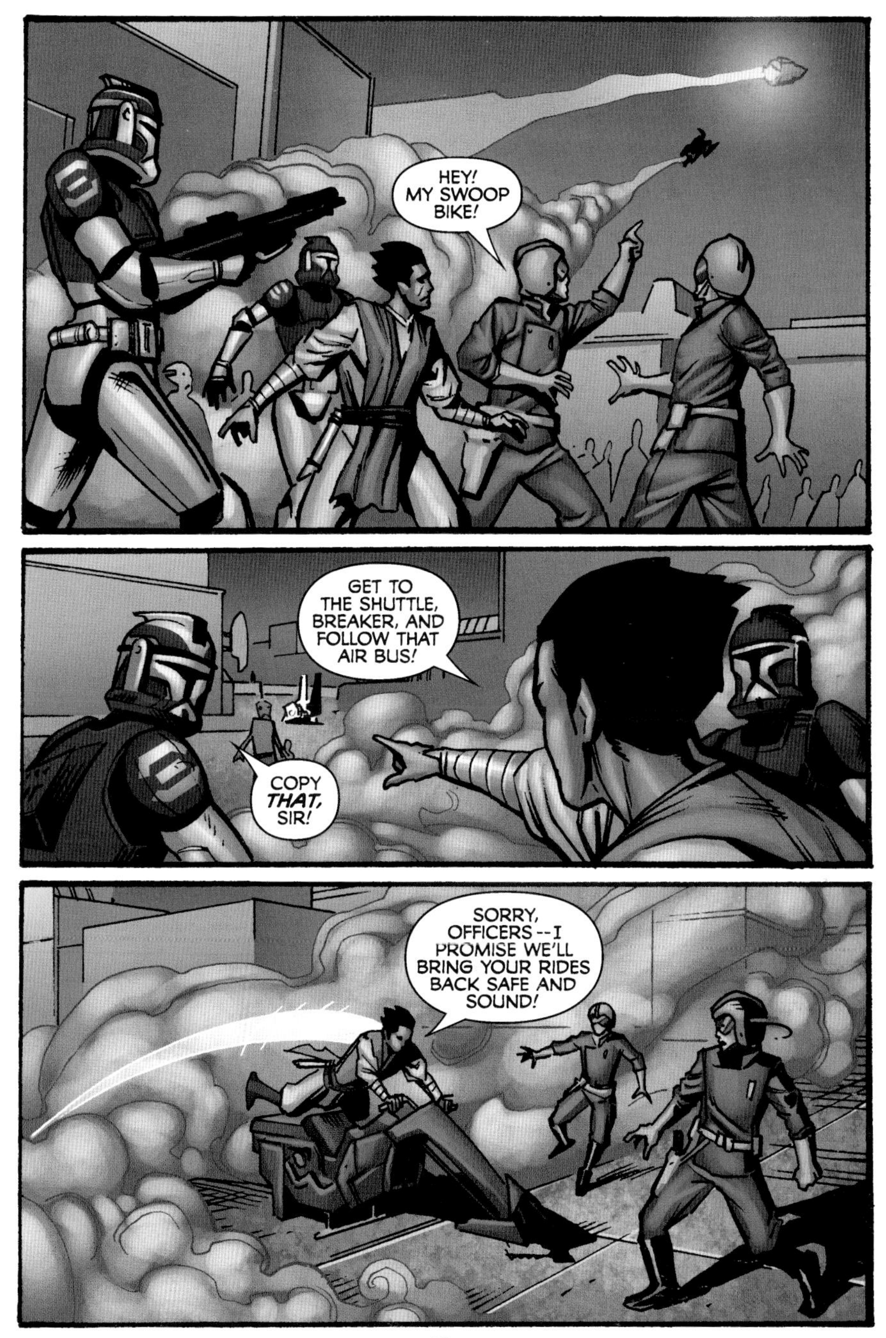
HEY! MY SWOOP BIKE!
GET TO THE SHUTTLE, BREAKER, AND FOLLOW THAT AIR BUS!
COPY THAT, SIR!
SORRY, OFFICERS--I PROMISE WE'LL BRING YOUR RIDES BACK SAFE AND SOUND!

CRAZY LUMMOX! YOU'RE GOING THE WRONG WAY!
GRRRRR! WHY WON'T THIS THING CLIMB?!
CLIMB... CLIMB...!
THOOM!
POODOO!

YIKES!
LOOK OUT!
UNF!
GIZZ A KNUCKLEHEAD.
ARE YOU ALL RIGHT?!
DON'T I LOOK IT?
I HOPE *YOUR* SWOOP'S VERTICAL THRUSTERS ARE WORKING!
CLIMB ON.

COME ON! JUICE IT!
I WANT MORE THAN A WORD WITH THAT TWI'LEK SHE-DEVIL!
DON'T LET YOUR EMOTIONS CLOUD YOUR JUDGMENT. IT'S POSSIBLE THERE HAS BEEN AN UNFORTUNATE MISUNDERSTANDING.
YEAH, YEAH, YEAH! JUST REMEMBER WHAT I SAID ABOUT WHEN YOU'VE GOT SOMEONE ON THE RUN!
GIZZ COMING.
HUH? IS HE TRYING TO KILL YOU AGAIN?

WE'RE BEING FOLLOWED! I *TOLD* YOU WE SHOULD HAVE RUN WHEN WE HAD THE CHANCE!
FASTER! WE CAN STILL MAKE IT TO YOUR CRUISER.
THE JEDI WON'T TOUCH US...

...SO LONG AS WE HAVE THE *LITTLE ONES.*

MAYBE WE SHOULD HAVE STAYED ON ABREGADO-RAE?

GIZZ, TAKE THE CONTROLS!
YOU GOT IT, KID!

LAND THE BUS IMMEDIATELY!
VMMM
AAAGH!
DOOL PUNDAR?!
THE JEDI?!

THANK THE STARS! THE JEDI HAS COME TO RESCUE US!
OUCH! STOP IT! YAAGH!
CAREFUL, NURU!
!

NO--YOU BE CAREFUL, GIZZ!
RAWR!

UNNH!
WAAGH!

PUNDAR'S KNOCKED OUT! I'LL GET THE CONTROLS!
WHAT'S WRONG, KUVUTA? DIDN'T THINK YOU'D SEE ME AGAIN?
GIZZ! WHERE ARE YOU? THAT AWFUL PILOT...HE TRIED TO KIDNAP THE CHILDREN AND ME!

ARE THE CHILDREN SAFE? DID YOU CAPTURE THE PILOT? OH, GIZZ, WHY WON'T YOU *SPEAK* TO ME?
YOU JUST DON'T KNOW WHEN TO QUIT, KUVUTA.
*UHNN...*WHAT HAPPENED?!
BEFORE YOU TIE YOUR BRAIN TAILS INTO A *KNOT* THINKING UP ANOTHER LIE...
...YOU MADE A BIG MISTAKE WHEN YOU TOLD THE KIDS TO TAKE THE *GREEN* AIR BUS.
YOU *FOOL!* THIS IS *ALL* YOUR FAULT!
I...I'M NOT *TOTALLY* BLIND, GIZZ. I CAN MAKE OUT COLORS... SHAPES.
I CAN TELL YOU...YOU ARE AS HANDSOME AS YOU ARE STRONG.
HER TOTAL LIAR. SHE NOT BLIND.
YOU UGLY.

COMMANDER?
GLAD YOU COULD JOIN US, BREAKER. TURNS OUT MISTRESS PINDI WAS WORKING IN LEAGUE WITH DOOL PUNDAR -- SUPPLYING HIM WITH SLAVES...
THE TWI'LEK HAD PROMISED ME FRESH RECRUITS ON FONDOR, WHERE I WAS ALREADY WAITING FOR NOGGOX'S FREIGHTER. BUT AFTER I WAS FORCED TO ABANDON MY BATTLESHIP --
-- SHE TRANSMITTED INSTRUCTIONS TO MEET HER ON FOLESS. I LANDED MY CRUISER AWAY FROM THE SPACEPORT TO AVOID THE LOCAL AUTHORITIES.
BREAKER, CONTACT GENERAL FISTO AND TELL HIM WE'VE CAPTURED DOOL PUNDAR.
HA! I'D LIKE TO SEE THE LOOK ON FISTO'S FACE WHEN HE LEARNS HE MISSED THE PARTY!
FISTO UGLY, TOO?
NOBODY MOVE, OR THE YOUNGLING DIES!

NICE KNIFE. I SHOULD'VE FRISKED YOU.
IN YOUR DREAMS! I'M GOING TO PUNDAR'S CRUISER, AND NO ONE BETTER TRY TO STOP ME!
AAGH! YOU LITTLE--!
CHOMP!
MISTRESS PINDI TASTE YUCKY.
STAY WITH THE CHILDREN AND GUARD PUNDAR!

!
GIZZ! WAIT! THERE'S A *DANGER SIGN!*
TELL MISTRESS PINDI TO STOP!
THE TRANDOSHAN BRAT WAS RIGHT... I CAN SEE JUST FINE!
YOU RUINED MY PLANS, GIZZ. AND NOW YOU'LL PAY WITH YOUR LIFE!
BEFORE YOU BLAST ME, KUVUTA, PLEASE HEAR ME OUT.
BEFORE I DIE, THERE'S JUST ONE THING I WANT YOU TO KNOW...
MISTRESS PINDI! *BEHIND YOU!*

NICE TRY, JEDI! BUT YOU CAN'T FOOL--
KA-CHOMP!
URRP

IT...IT'S NOT YOUR FAULT, GIZZ. SHE...SHE DIDN'T SEE THE SIGN EITHER.
WELL, I... I'LL MEET YOU BACK AT THE SHIP.
THE ONE THING I WANTED YOU TO KNOW...
I *DID* SEE THE SIGN. SAW THAT MONSTER BEHIND YOU, TOO.

ALL THE ORPHANS HAVE BEEN PLACED WITH RESPONSIBLE FAMILIES?
YES, CHANCELLOR. AND DOOL PUNDAR IS IN PRISON. AS FOR WHO KILLED NOGGOX THE HUTT...
...OUR INVESTIGATION CONTINUES. MEANWHILE, REPUBLIC TECHNICIANS HAVE NOGGOX'S DROID FACTORY UP AND RUNNING AGAIN.
THANK YOU, GENERAL FISTO. YOUR SERVICE TO THE REPUBLIC IS COMMENDABLE.
AS MY REPORT INDICATES, CHANCELLOR, ALL THE CREDIT FOR THE SUCCESS OF THIS MISSION MUST GO TO NURU KUNGURAMA AND BREAKOUT SQUAD.
MIGHT I SPEAK WITH KUNGURAMA, TO EXPRESS MY APPRECIATION?
UNAVAILABLE AT PRESENT, HE IS. TOLD US, HE DID...

"...AN IMPORTANT MEETING WITH A FRIEND, HE HAS."
I'M SERIOUS, KID. I'M THROUGH WITH THEM. DONE! FINISHED!
IF THE MOST DROP-DEAD GORGEOUS ZELTRON PARTY GIRL WERE TO SLINK UP TO ME RIGHT NOW AND SAY, "LET'S DANCE," YOU KNOW WHAT I'D SAY?
"SURE."
OH, NO, I WOULDN'T! I'D SAY, "GET LOST!" THEN I'D --
HEY-- WHY'RE WE HEADING FOR DEXTER'S DINER?
THERE'S PLENTY OF OTHER JOINTS NEARBY. WHY DON'T WE TRY SOMEPLACE DIFFERENT.
DEXTER TOLD ME HE WAS FIXING UP SOMETHING SPECIAL TODAY. COME ON.

WELL, LOOK WHO'S *BACK.*
NURU WAS IN HERE EARLIER. I OVERHEARD HIM TALKING WITH DEXTER ...SOMETHING ABOUT YOU RESCUING A SHIPLOAD OF *ORPHANS?*
IF THAT'S *TRUE,* GIZZ, WOULD YOU LIKE A *HERO'S DINNER?* MY TREAT?
SURE.
THE END

PRESIDENT AND PUBLISHER **MIKE RICHARDSON**

EXECUTIVE VICE PRESIDENT **NEIL HANKERSON**

CHIEF FINANCIAL OFFICER **TOM WEDDLE**

VICE PRESIDENT OF PUBLISHING **RANDY STRADLEY**

VICE PRESIDENT OF BOOK TRADE SALES **MICHAEL MARTENS**

VICE PRESIDENT OF BUSINESS AFFAIRS **ANITA NELSON**

VICE PRESIDENT OF MARKETING **MICHA HERSHMAN**

VICE PRESIDENT OF PRODUCT DEVELOPMENT **DAVID SCROGGY**

VICE PRESIDENT OF INFORMATION TECHNOLOGY **DALE LAFOUNTAIN**

SENIOR DIRECTOR OF PRINT, DESIGN, AND PRODUCTION **DARLENE VOGEL**

GENERAL COUNSEL **KEN LIZZI**

EDITORIAL DIRECTOR **DAVEY ESTRADA**

SENIOR MANAGING EDITOR **SCOTT ALLIE**

SENIOR BOOKS EDITOR **CHRIS WARNER**

EXECUTIVE EDITOR **DIANA SCHUTZ**

DIRECTOR OF PRINT AND DEVELOPMENT **CARY GRAZZINI**

ART DIRECTOR **LIA RIBACCHI**

DIRECTOR OF SCHEDULING **CARA NIECE**

STAR WARS GRAPHIC NOVEL TIMELINE (IN YEARS)

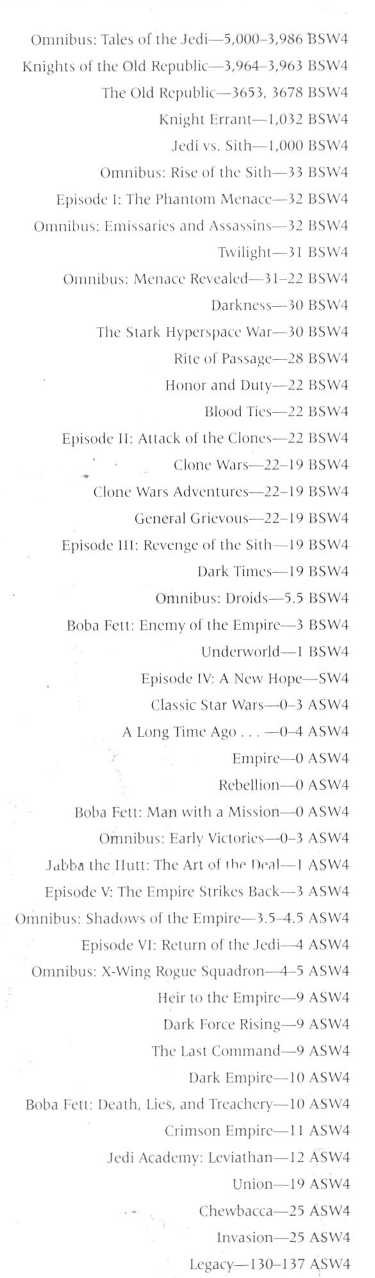
Omnibus: Tales of the Jedi—5,000–3,986 BSW4
Knights of the Old Republic—3,964–3,963 BSW4
The Old Republic—3653, 3678 BSW4
Knight Errant—1,032 BSW4
Jedi vs. Sith—1,000 BSW4
Omnibus: Rise of the Sith—33 BSW4
Episode I: The Phantom Menace—32 BSW4
Omnibus: Emissaries and Assassins—32 BSW4
Twilight—31 BSW4
Omnibus: Menace Revealed—31–22 BSW4
Darkness—30 BSW4
The Stark Hyperspace War—30 BSW4
Rite of Passage—28 BSW4
Honor and Duty—22 BSW4
Blood Ties—22 BSW4
Episode II: Attack of the Clones—22 BSW4
Clone Wars—22–19 BSW4
Clone Wars Adventures—22–19 BSW4
General Grievous—22–19 BSW4
Episode III: Revenge of the Sith—19 BSW4
Dark Times—19 BSW4
Omnibus: Droids—5.5 BSW4
Boba Fett: Enemy of the Empire—3 BSW4
Underworld—1 BSW4
Episode IV: A New Hope—SW4
Classic Star Wars—0–3 ASW4
A Long Time Ago . . . —0–4 ASW4
Empire—0 ASW4
Rebellion—0 ASW4
Boba Fett: Man with a Mission—0 ASW4
Omnibus: Early Victories—0–3 ASW4
Jabba the Hutt: The Art of the Deal—1 ASW4
Episode V: The Empire Strikes Back—3 ASW4
Omnibus: Shadows of the Empire—3.5–4.5 ASW4
Episode VI: Return of the Jedi—4 ASW4
Omnibus: X-Wing Rogue Squadron—4–5 ASW4
Heir to the Empire—9 ASW4
Dark Force Rising—9 ASW4
The Last Command—9 ASW4
Dark Empire—10 ASW4
Boba Fett: Death, Lies, and Treachery—10 ASW4
Crimson Empire—11 ASW4
Jedi Academy: Leviathan—12 ASW4
Union—19 ASW4
Chewbacca—25 ASW4
Invasion—25 ASW4
Legacy—130–137 ASW4

Old Republic Era
25,000 – 1000 years before
Star Wars: A New Hope

Rise of the Empire Era
1000 – 0 years before
Star Wars: A New Hope

Rebellion Era
0 – 5 years after
Star Wars: A New Hope

New Republic Era
5 – 25 years after
Star Wars: A New Hope

New Jedi Order Era
25+ years after
Star Wars: A New Hope

Legacy Era
130+ years after
Star Wars: A New Hope

Vector
Crosses four eras in the timeline

Volume 1
Knights of the Old Republic Volume 5
Dark Times Volume 3

Volume 2
Rebellion Volume 4
Legacy Volume 6

BSW4 = before *Episode IV: A New Hope*. ASW4 = after *Episode IV: A New Hope*.